The Po
The Chord So

£1

47

Wise Publications
London/New York/Paris/Sydney/Copenhagen/Madrid/Tokyo

Exclusive Distributors:

Music Sales Limited
8/9 Frith Street,
London W1D 3JB, England.
Music Sales Pty Limited
120 Rothschild Avenue,
Rosebery, NSW 2018, Australia.

Order No. AM971223
ISBN 0-7119-8955-9
This book © Copyright 2001 by Wise Publications

Compiled by Nick Crispin
Music arranged by Rikky Rooksby
Music engraved by The Pitts

Cover photograph courtesy of Rex Features London.

Printed in the United Kingdom by
Caligraving Limited, Thetford, Nolfolk.

Your Guarantee of Quality
As publishers, we strive to produce every book
to the highest commercial standards.
This book has been carefully designed to minimise awkward
page turns and to make playing from it a real pleasure.
Particular care has been given to specifying acid-free,
neutral-sized paper made from pulps which have not been
elemental chlorine bleached. This pulp is from farmed sustainable
forests and was produced with special regard for the environment.
Throughout, the printing and binding have been planned to
ensure a sturdy, attractive publication which should give years
of enjoyment. If your copy fails to meet our high standards,
please inform us and we will gladly replace it.

Music Sales' complete catalogue describes thousands
of titles and is available in full colour sections by subject,
direct from Music Sales Limited. Please state your areas of interest
and send a cheque/postal order for £1.50 for postage to:
Music Sales Limited, Newmarket Road,
Bury St. Edmunds, Suffolk IP33 3YB.

www.musicsales.com

Relative Tuning

The guitar can be tuned with the aid of pitch pipes or dedicated electronic guitar tuners which are available through your local music dealer. If you do not have a tuning device, you can use relative tuning. Estimate the pitch of the 6th string as near as possible to E or at least a comfortable pitch (not too high, as you might break other strings in tuning up). Then, while checking the various positions on the diagram, place a finger from your left hand on the:

5th fret of the E or 6th string and **tune the open A** (or 5th string) to the note Ⓐ

5th fret of the A or 5th string and **tune the open D** (or 4th string) to the note Ⓓ

5th fret of the D or 4th string and **tune the open G** (or 3rd string) to the note Ⓖ

4th fret of the G or 3rd string and **tune the open B** (or 2nd string) to the note Ⓑ

5th fret of the B or 2nd string and **tune the open E** (or 1st string) to the note Ⓔ

Reading Chord Boxes

Chord boxes are diagrams of the guitar neck viewed head upwards, face on as illustrated. The top horizontal line is the nut, unless a higher fret number is indicated, the others are the frets.

The vertical lines are the strings, starting from E (or 6th) on the left to E (or 1st) on the right.

The black dots indicate where to place your fingers.

Strings marked with an O are played open, not fretted. Strings marked with an X should not be played.

The curved bracket indicates a 'barre' – hold down the strings under the bracket with your first finger, using your other fingers to fret the remaining notes.

4

Can't Stand Losing You

Words & Music by
Sting

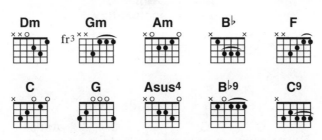

Intro | Dm Gm | Dm Gm | Dm Gm | Dm Gm ||

Verse 1

   Dm   Am   Gm
Called you so many times today

      Dm   Am   Gm
And I guess it's all true what your girl friends say,

      Dm   Am   Gm
That you don't ever want so see me again,

         Dm   Am   Gm
And your brother's gonna kill me and he's six foot ten,

    B♭   F   B♭   F
I guess you'd call it cowardice

             C   G   C   Asus⁴
But I'm not prepared to go on like this.

Chorus 1

    B♭
I can't, I can't, I can't stand losing,

   Gm
I can't, I can't, I can't stand losing,

Asus⁴   Dm   Gm
I can't, I can't, I can't, I can't stand losing   you,

Dm   Gm Dm   Gm
   I can't stand losing you,

Dm Gm   Dm   Gm
   I can't stand losing you,

Dm Gm   Dm   Gm   Dm Gm
   I can't stand losing you.

Verse 2

      Dm   **Am**   **Gm**
I see you've sent my letters back,

        Dm Am   **Gm**
And my L.P. records and they're all scratched.

    Dm   **Am**   **Gm**
I can't see the point in another day,

       Dm   **Am**   **Gm**
When nobody listens to a word I say.

          B♭ **F**   **B♭** **F**
You can call it lack of confidence

         C   **G**   **C**   **Asus⁴**
But to carry on living doesn't make no sense.

Chorus 2

      B♭
I can't, I can't, I can't stand losing,

      Gm
I can't, I can't, I can't stand losing,

      Asus⁴
I can't, I can't, I can't stand losing,

      B♭
I can't, I can't, I can't stand losing,

      Gm
I can't, I can't, I can't stand losing,

      Asus⁴
I can't, I can't, I can't stand losing.

Instrumental ‖: **B♭9** | **B♭9** | **C9** | **C9** :‖

Middle

      Dm
I guess this is our last goodbye,

And you don't care so I won't cry,

And you'll be sorry when I'm dead

And all this guilt will blow your head.

      B♭   **F**   **B♭** **F**
I guess you'd call it suicide

      C   **G**   **C**   **Asus⁴**
But I'm too full to swallow my pride.

Chorus 3

B♭
I can't, I can't, I can't stand losing,

Gm
I can't, I can't, I can't stand losing,

Asus⁴
I can't, I can't, I can't stand losing,

B♭
I can't, I can't, I can't stand losing,

Gm
I can't, I can't, I can't stand losing,

Asus⁴
I can't, I can't, I can't stand losing,

C
Outro   ‖: I can't, I can't, I can't stand losing,

Asus⁴
I can't, I can't, I can't stand losing,

B♭
I can't, I can't, I can't stand losing. :‖ *Repeat to fade*

The Bed's Too Big Without You

Words & Music by
Sting

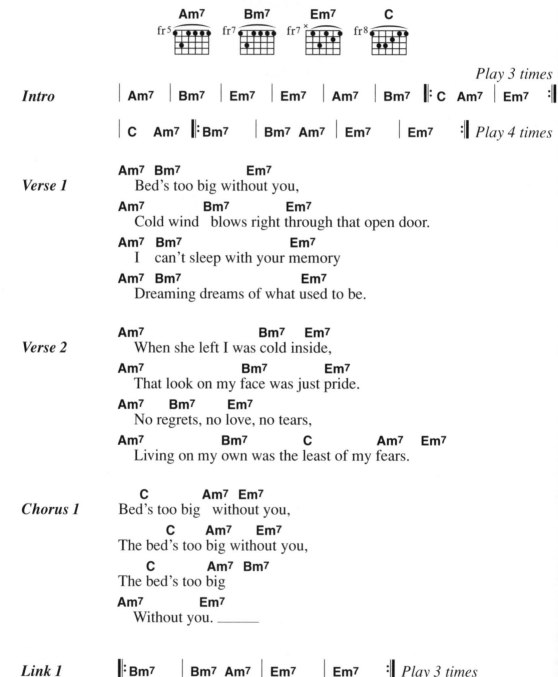

Play 3 times

Intro
| Am7 | Bm7 | Em7 | Em7 | Am7 | Bm7 ‖: C Am7 | Em7 :‖

| C Am7 ‖: Bm7 | Bm7 Am7 | Em7 | Em7 :‖ *Play 4 times*

Verse 1

Am7 Bm7   Em7
Bed's too big without you,

Am7   Bm7   Em7
Cold wind   blows right through that open door.

Am7 Bm7   Em7
I   can't sleep with your memory

Am7 Bm7   Em7
Dreaming dreams of what used to be.

Verse 2

Am7   Bm7   Em7
When she left I was cold inside,

Am7   Bm7   Em7
That look on my face was just pride.

Am7   Bm7   Em7
No regrets, no love, no tears,

Am7   Bm7   C   Am7 Em7
Living on my own was the least of my fears.

Chorus 1

        C   Am7 Em7
Bed's too big   without you,

        C   Am7   Em7
The bed's too big without you,

        C   Am7 Bm7
The bed's too big

Am7   Em7
Without you. _____

Link 1
‖: Bm7 | Bm7 Am7 | Em7 | Em7 :‖ *Play 3 times*

© Copyright 1979 Magnetic Publishing Limited/EMI Music Publishing Limited.
All Rights Reserved. International Copyright Secured.

8

Verse 3

Am7   Bm7   Em7
Since that day when you'd gone,

Am7 Bm7 Em7
Just had to carry on.

Am7   Bm7 Em7
I get through the day but late at night

Am7   Bm7 Em7
Made love to my pillow but it didn't feel right.

Verse 4

Am7 Bm7 Em7
Every day, just the same:

Am7   Bm7 Em7
Old rules for the same old game.

Am7 Bm7 Em7
All I gained was heartache,

Am7 Bm7   C Am7 Em7
All I made was one mistake.

Chorus 2

     C   Am7 Em7
Now the bed's too big without you,

   C Am7 Em7
The bed's too big without you,

   C   Am7 Bm7
The bed's too big

Am7   Em7
Without you. _____

Link 2 ‖: Bm7 | Bm7 Am7 | Em7 | Em7 :‖ *Play 3 times*

Instrumental | Drums and bass for 32 bars ‖ C Am7 | Em7   ‖

Chorus 3 As Chorus 1

Coda ‖: Bm7 Am7   Em7 :‖
           Without you. _____

    ‖: Bm7 | Bm7 Am7 | Em7 | Em7 :‖

Am7 Bm7   Em7
The bed's too big without you,

Am7   Bm7 Em7
Cold wind blows right through that open door.

              Fade out

Born In The 50's

Words & Music by
Sting

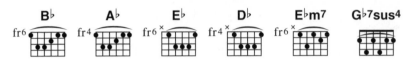

Chorus 1

Bb Ab Eb
We were born,

    Bb   Ab
Born in the fifties.

Eb   Db Ab
Born, born in the fif - ties,

Eb   Bb Ab
Born, born in the fifties,

Eb   Db Ab
Born, born in the fif - ties.

Verse 1

Eb   Ab
 My mother cried

  Bb   Ab
When President Kennedy died,

  Eb   Ab
She said it was the Communists

   Bb
But I knew better.

Eb   Ab
 Would they drop the bomb on us

    Bb   Ab
While we made love on the beach?

    Eb   Ab
We were the class they couldn't teach

    Bb
'Cause we knew better.

Chorus 2   As Chorus 1

Verse 2

       E♭   **A♭**
They screamed

           B♭   **A♭**
When the Beatles sang,

         E♭   **A♭**
And they laughed when the King fell down the stairs.

         B♭
Oh, they should've known better.

A♭   **E♭**   **A♭**
  Oh, we hated our aunts

         B♭   **A♭**
Then we messed in our pants,

         E♭   **A♭**
Then we lost our faith and prayed to the TV,

         B♭
Oh, we should've known better.

Chorus 3   As Chorus 1

Bridge

E♭m7   **A♭**
  We freeze like statues on the pages of history,

E♭m7   **A♭**
  Living was never like this when we took all those G. C. Es.

E♭m7
Oh, you opened the door for us

G♭7sus4
  And then you turned to dust.

      B♭
You don't understand us

So don't reprimand us;

We're taking the future,

We don't need no teacher.

Outro

     E♭   **B♭**   **A♭**
‖: Born, born in the fifties.

E♭   **D♭**   **A♭**
Born, born in the fif - ties.   :‖ *Repeat to fade*

Bring On The Night

Words & Music by
Sting

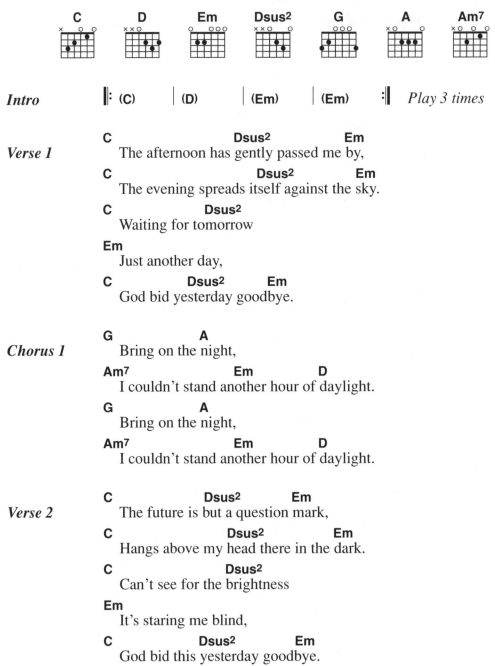

Intro ‖: (C) | (D) | (Em) | (Em) :‖ *Play 3 times*

Verse 1

C   Dsus2   Em
The afternoon has gently passed me by,

C   Dsus2   Em
The evening spreads itself against the sky.

C   Dsus2
Waiting for tomorrow

Em
Just another day,

C   Dsus2   Em
God bid yesterday goodbye.

Chorus 1

G   A
Bring on the night,

Am7   Em   D
I couldn't stand another hour of daylight.

G   A
Bring on the night,

Am7   Em   D
I couldn't stand another hour of daylight.

Verse 2

C   Dsus2   Em
The future is but a question mark,

C   Dsus2   Em
Hangs above my head there in the dark.

C   Dsus2
Can't see for the brightness

Em
It's staring me blind,

C   Dsus2   Em
God bid this yesterday goodbye.

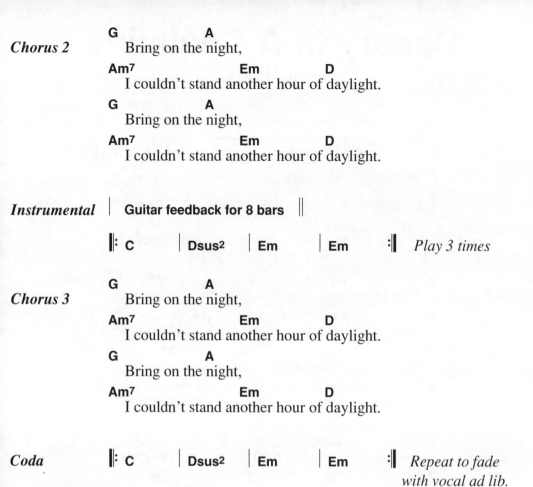

Chorus 2

    G   **A**
Bring on the night,

Am⁷   **Em**   **D**
I couldn't stand another hour of daylight.

G   **A**
Bring on the night,

Am⁷   **Em**   **D**
I couldn't stand another hour of daylight.

Instrumental | **Guitar feedback for 8 bars** ‖

‖: **C** | **Dsus²** | **Em** | **Em**   :‖ *Play 3 times*

Chorus 3

G   **A**
Bring on the night,

Am⁷   **Em**   **D**
I couldn't stand another hour of daylight.

G   **A**
Bring on the night,

Am⁷   **Em**   **D**
I couldn't stand another hour of daylight.

Coda   ‖: **C** | **Dsus²** | **Em** | **Em**   :‖ *Repeat to fade*
                                                       with vocal ad lib.

Canary In A Coalmine

Words & Music by
Sting

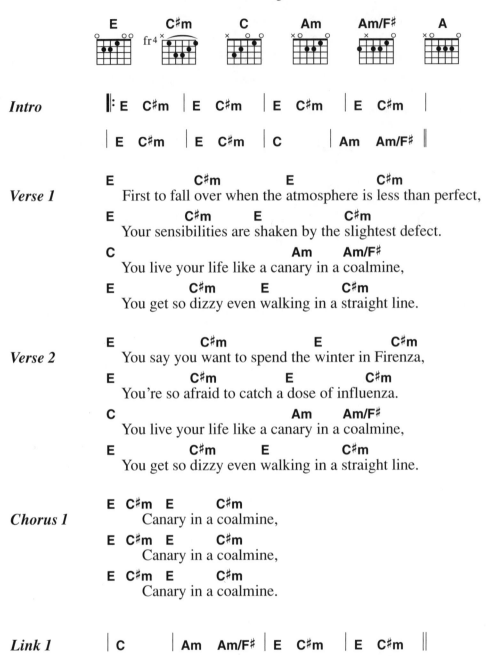

Intro

| E C#m | E C#m | E C#m | E C#m |

| E C#m | E C#m | C | Am Am/F# ||

Verse 1

E   C#m   E   C#m
First to fall over when the atmosphere is less than perfect,
E   C#m   E   C#m
Your sensibilities are shaken by the slightest defect.
C   Am Am/F#
You live your life like a canary in a coalmine,
E   C#m   E   C#m
You get so dizzy even walking in a straight line.

Verse 2

E   C#m   E   C#m
You say you want to spend the winter in Firenza,
E   C#m   E   C#m
You're so afraid to catch a dose of influenza.
C   Am Am/F#
You live your life like a canary in a coalmine,
E   C#m   E   C#m
You get so dizzy even walking in a straight line.

Chorus 1

E C#m E C#m
Canary in a coalmine,
E C#m E C#m
Canary in a coalmine,
E C#m E C#m
Canary in a coalmine.

Link 1

| C | Am Am/F# | E C#m | E C#m ||

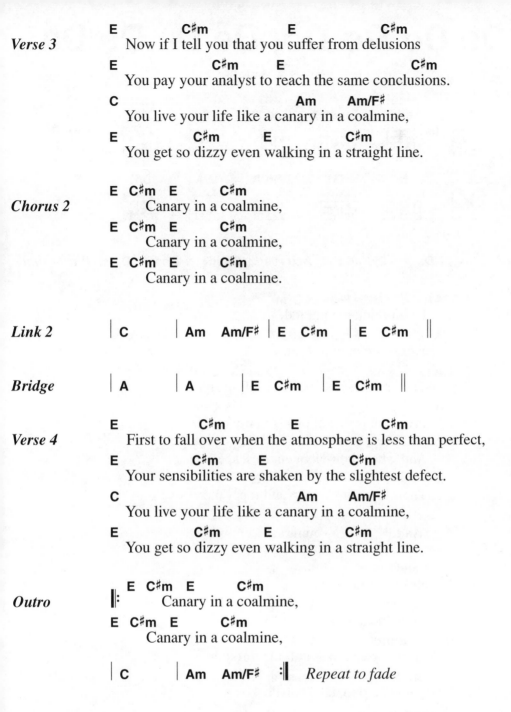

Verse 3

```
        E           C#m              E              C#m
        Now if I tell you that you suffer from delusions
        E              C#m        E                   C#m
        You pay your analyst to reach the same conclusions.
        C                           Am      Am/F#
        You live your life like a canary in a coalmine,
        E           C#m        E              C#m
        You get so dizzy even walking in a straight line.
```

Chorus 2

```
        E  C#m  E      C#m
        Canary in a coalmine,
        E  C#m  E      C#m
        Canary in a coalmine,
        E  C#m  E      C#m
        Canary in a coalmine.
```

Link 2

```
        | C        | Am   Am/F# | E  C#m  | E  C#m   ||
```

Bridge

```
        | A        | A          | E  C#m  | E  C#m   ||
```

Verse 4

```
        E           C#m              E              C#m
        First to fall over when the atmosphere is less than perfect,
        E              C#m        E              C#m
        Your sensibilities are shaken by the slightest defect.
        C                           Am      Am/F#
        You live your life like a canary in a coalmine,
        E           C#m        E              C#m
        You get so dizzy even walking in a straight line.
```

Outro

```
      ‖: E  C#m  E      C#m
           Canary in a coalmine,
        E  C#m  E      C#m
        Canary in a coalmine,

        | C        | Am   Am/F# :‖  Repeat to fade
```

De Do Do Do, De Da Da Da

Words & Music by
Sting

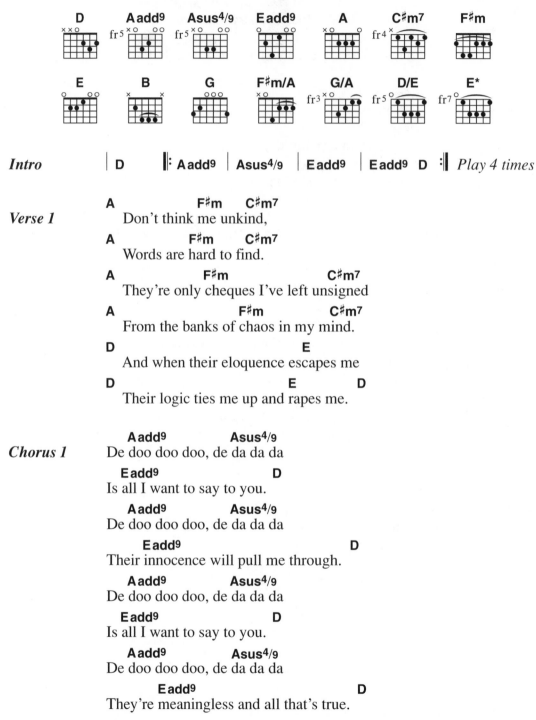

Intro | D ‖: A add⁹ | Asus⁴/₉ | E add⁹ | E add⁹ D :‖ *Play 4 times*

Verse 1

A   F#m   C#m⁷
Don't think me unkind,

A   F#m   C#m⁷
Words are hard to find.

A   F#m   C#m⁷
They're only cheques I've left unsigned

A   F#m   C#m⁷
From the banks of chaos in my mind.

D   E
And when their eloquence escapes me

D   E   D
Their logic ties me up and rapes me.

Chorus 1

A add⁹   Asus⁴/₉
De doo doo doo, de da da da

E add⁹   D
Is all I want to say to you.

A add⁹   Asus⁴/₉
De doo doo doo, de da da da

E add⁹   D
Their innocence will pull me through.

A add⁹   Asus⁴/₉
De doo doo doo, de da da da

E add⁹   D
Is all I want to say to you.

A add⁹   Asus⁴/₉
De doo doo doo, de da da da

E add⁹   D
They're meaningless and all that's true.

Verse 2

A F♯m   C♯m7
Poets, priests and politicians

A   F♯m   C♯m7
Have words to thank for their positions,

A F♯m   C♯m7
Words that scream for your submission

A   F♯m   C♯m7
And no one's jamming their transmission.

D   E
'Cause when their eloquence escapes you

D   E D
Their logic ties you up and rapes you.

Chorus 2

 Aadd9   Asus4/9
De doo doo doo, de da da da

Eadd9   D
Is all I want to say to you.

 Aadd9   Asus4/9
De doo doo doo, de da da da

 Eadd9   D
Their innocence will pu hrough.

 Aadd9   Asus4,
De doo doo doo, de da da d.

Eadd9   D
Is all I want to say to you.

 Aadd9   Asus4/9
De doo doo doo, de da da da

  Eadd9
They're meaningless and all that's true. ___

Link

| B | G | A | E | B | G | |

| F♯m/A G/A | F♯m/A G/A | F♯m/A G/A | F♯m/A G/A |

| D/E E* | D/E E* | D/E E* | D/E E* D ‖

Chorus 3 As Chorus 1

Coda ‖: A | F♯m | C♯m7 | C♯m7 :‖

Don't Stand So Close To Me

Words & Music by
Sting

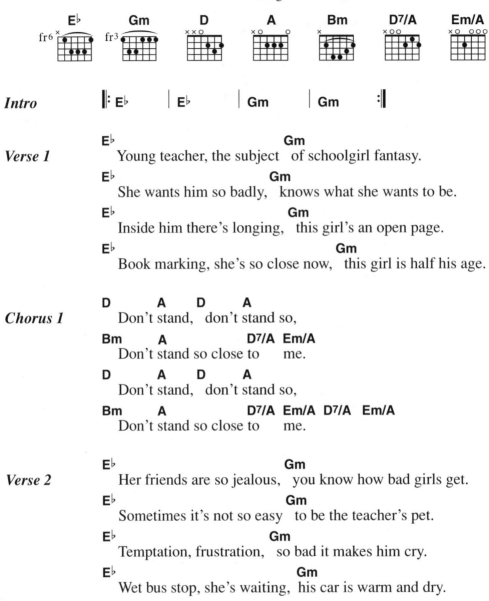

Intro   ‖: E♭ | E♭ | Gm | Gm :‖

Verse 1

E♭   Gm
Young teacher, the subject   of schoolgirl fantasy.

E♭   Gm
She wants him so badly,   knows what she wants to be.

E♭   Gm
Inside him there's longing,   this girl's an open page.

E♭   Gm
Book marking, she's so close now,   this girl is half his age.

Chorus 1

D   A   D   A
Don't stand,   don't stand so,

Bm   A   D7/A Em/A
Don't stand so close to   me.

D   A   D   A
Don't stand,   don't stand so,

Bm   A   D7/A Em/A D7/A Em/A
Don't stand so close to   me.

Verse 2

E♭   Gm
Her friends are so jealous,   you know how bad girls get.

E♭   Gm
Sometimes it's not so easy   to be the teacher's pet.

E♭   Gm
Temptation, frustration,   so bad it makes him cry.

E♭   Gm
Wet bus stop, she's waiting, his car is warm and dry.

Chorus 2

    D   **A**   **D**   **A**
    Don't stand, don't stand so,
    Bm   **A**   **D7/A Em/A**
    Don't stand so close to   me.
    D   **A**   **D**   **A**
    Don't stand, don't stand so,
    Bm   **A**   **D7/A Em/A D7/A Em/A**
    Don't stand so close to   me.

Verse 3

    E♭   **Gm**
    Loose talk in the classroom,   to hurt they try and try.
    E♭   **Gm**
    Strong words in the staff-room,   the accusations fly.
    E♭   **Gm**
    It's no use, he sees her,   he starts to shake and cough
    E♭   **Gm**
    Just like the old man in   that book by Nabakov.

Chorus 3

    D   **A**   **D**   **A**
    Don't stand, don't stand so,
    Bm   **A**   **D7/A Em/A**
    Don't stand so close to   me.
    D   **A**   **D**   **A**
    Don't stand, don't stand so,
    Bm   **A**   **D7/A Em/A**
    Don't stand so close to   me.

    | **D7/A Em/A** | **D7/A Em/A** | **D7/A Em/A** ‖

Instrumental ‖: **E♭** | **E♭** | **Gm** | **Gm**   :‖ *Play 4 times*

Outro

    ‖: **D**   **A**   **D**   **A**
      Don't stand,   don't   stand so,
      (Please __ don't __ stand ___ so ___
    Bm   **A**   **D7/A Em/A**
      Don't stand so close to   me.
      Close ___ to   me.)   :‖ *Repeat to fade*

Driven To Tears

Words & Music by
Sting

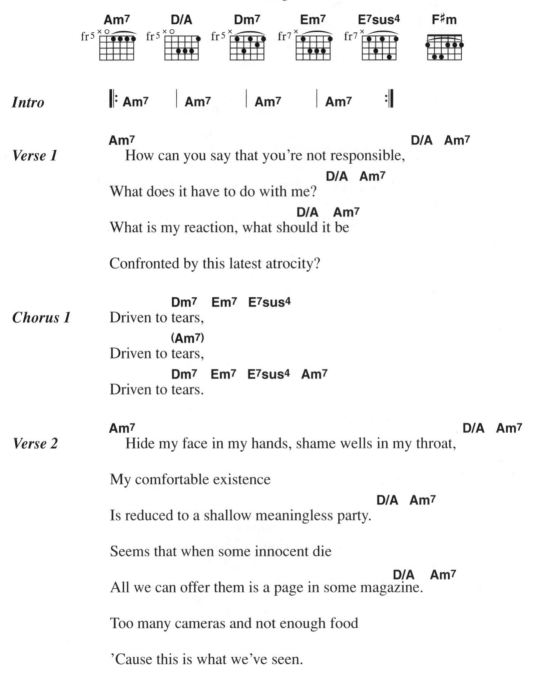

Intro
‖: Am7 | Am7 | Am7 | Am7 :‖

Verse 1

Am7   D/A Am7
    How can you say that you're not responsible,

                                 D/A Am7
What does it have to do with me?

                            D/A   Am7
What is my reaction, what should it be

Confronted by this latest atrocity?

Chorus 1

           Dm7   Em7   E7sus4
Driven to tears,

          (Am7)
Driven to tears,

          Dm7   Em7   E7sus4   Am7
Driven to tears.

Verse 2

Am7   D/A Am7
    Hide my face in my hands, shame wells in my throat,

My comfortable existence

                                D/A Am7
Is reduced to a shallow meaningless party.

Seems that when some innocent die

                                  D/A Am7
All we can offer them is a page in some magazine.

Too many cameras and not enough food

'Cause this is what we've seen.

Chorus 2

        Dm7 Em7 E7sus4
Driven to tears,

        (Am7)
Driven to tears,

        Dm7 Em7 E7sus4 Am7
Driven to tears.

Link

| F#m | F#m | F#m | F#m | F#m | F#m |

Wo - oh - oh,   wo - oh - oh,   wo - oh - oh,

| F#m | Am7 ‖

wo - oh - oh.

Solo

‖: (Em7) | (Em7) | (Em7) | (Em7) :‖

Verse 3

Am7   **D/A Am7**
    Protest is futile, nothing seems to get through.

What's to become of our world, who knows what to do?

Chorus 3

        Dm7 Em7 E7sus4
‖: Driven to tears,

        (Am7)
Driven to tears,

        Dm7 Em7 E7sus4 Am7
Driven to tears.   :‖

Coda

‖: Am7 | Am7 | Am7 | Am7 :‖ *Play 4 times*

‖: Dm7 | Em7 E7sus4 | (Am7) | (Am7) :‖ *Play 3 times*

| Dm7 | Em7 E7sus4 | Am ‖

Every Breath You Take

Words & Music by
Sting

Gadd9   Emadd9   Csus2   Dsus2   Csus2/B♭   Aadd9   E♭   F

Intro

| Gadd9 | Gadd9 | Emadd9 | Emadd9 |

| Csus2 | Dsus2 | Gadd9 |

Verse 1

Gadd9
    Ev'ry breath you take,
           Emadd9
Ev'ry move you make,
           Csus2
Ev'ry bone you break,
         Dsus2
Ev'ry step you take,
          Emadd9
I'll be watching you.

        Gadd9
Ev'ry single day,
         Emadd9
Ev'ry word you say,
         Csus2
Ev'ry game you play,
        Dsus2
Ev'ry night you stay,
        Gadd9
I'll be watching you.

Chorus 1

Csus2
Oh, can't you see

Csus2/B♭   Gadd9
You belong to me,

Aadd9
How my poor heart aches

Dsus2
With ev'ry step you take.

Gadd9
Ev'ry move you make,

Emadd9
Ev'ry vow you break,

Csus2
Ev'ry smile you fake,

Dsus2
Ev'ry claim you stake

Emadd9
I'll be watching you.

Middle

E♭
Since you've gone, I've been lost without a trace,

F
I dream at night I can only see your face,

E♭
I look around but it's you I can't replace,

F
I feel so cold and I long for your embrace,

E♭
I keep crying baby, baby please.

Instrumental   ‖: Gadd9 | Gadd9 | Emadd9 | Emadd9 |

| Csus2 | Dsus2 | Gadd9 | Gadd9 :‖

Chorus 2   As Chorus 1

Outro

Emadd9   Csus2
Ev'ry move you make,

Dsus2
Ev'ry step you take

Emadd9
I'll be watching you.

Emadd9
I'll be watching

‖: Gadd9 | Gadd9 | Emadd9 | Csus2
you.   I'll be watching :‖ *Repeat to fade*

23

Invisible Sun

Words & Music by
sting

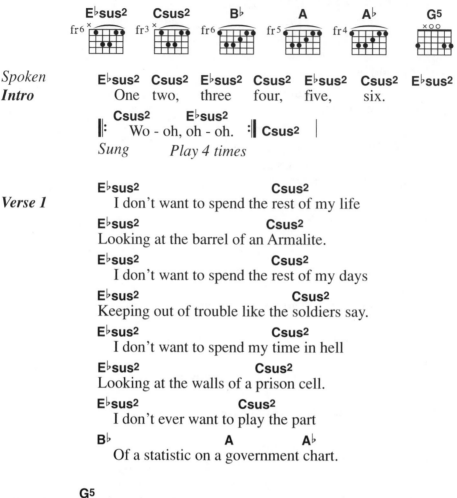

Spoken
Intro

| E♭sus2 | Csus2 | E♭sus2 | Csus2 | E♭sus2 | Csus2 | E♭sus2 |
| One | two, | three | four, | five, | six. | |

‖: Csus2 E♭sus2 :‖ Csus2 |
Wo - oh, oh - oh.

Sung   *Play 4 times*

Verse 1

E♭sus2   Csus2
  I don't want to spend the rest of my life

E♭sus2   Csus2
Looking at the barrel of an Armalite.

E♭sus2   Csus2
  I don't want to spend the rest of my days

E♭sus2   Csus2
Keeping out of trouble like the soldiers say.

E♭sus2   Csus2
  I don't want to spend my time in hell

E♭sus2   Csus2
Looking at the walls of a prison cell.

E♭sus2   Csus2
  I don't ever want to play the part

B♭   A   A♭
Of a statistic on a government chart.

Chorus 1

    G5
There has to be an invisible sun,

It gives it's heat to everyone.

There has to be an invisible sun,

That gives us hope when the whole day's done.

Verse 2

E♭sus2   **Csus2**
It's dark all day and it glows all night,

E♭sus2   **Csus2**
Factory smoke and acetylene light.

E♭sus2   **Csus2**
I face the day with my head caved in

B♭   **A**   **A♭**
Looking like something that the cat brought in.

Chorus 2   As Chorus 1

Instrumental 𝄆 E♭sus2 | Csus2 | E♭sus2 | Csus2 𝄇

Verse 3

E♭sus2   **Csus2**
And they're only going to change this place

   E♭sus2   **Csus2**
By killing everybody in the human race.

E♭sus2   **Csus2**
They would kill me for a cigarette

B♭   **A**   **A♭**
But I don't even wanna die just yet.

Chorus 3

G5
There has to be an invisible sun,

It gives it's heat to everyone.

There has to be an invisible sun,

That gives us hope when the whole day's (done.)

| **E♭sus2** | **Csus2** | **E♭sus2** ‖
done. _____

Coda 𝄆 **Csus2**   **E♭sus2**
      Wo - oh, oh - oh. 𝄇 *Repeat to fade*

Every Little Thing She Does Is Magic

Words & Music by
Sting

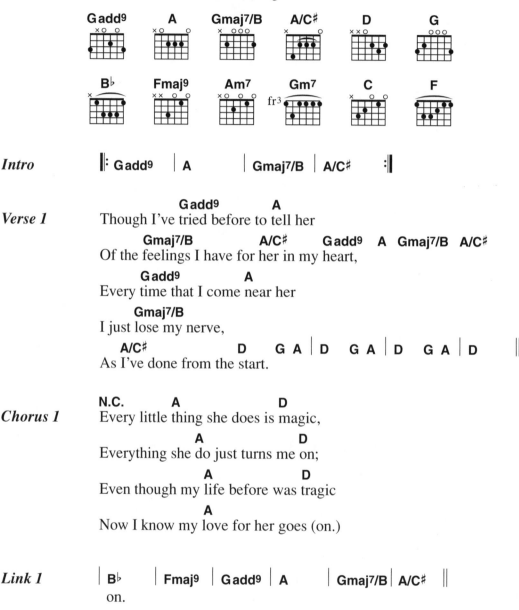

Intro ‖: Gadd⁹ | A | Gmaj⁷/B | A/C♯ :‖

Verse 1

Gadd⁹ A
Though I've tried before to tell her

Gmaj⁷/B   A/C♯ Gadd⁹ A Gmaj⁷/B A/C♯
Of the feelings I have for her in my heart,

Gadd⁹   A
Every time that I come near her

Gmaj⁷/B
I just lose my nerve,

A/C♯   D G A | D G A | D G A | D ‖
As I've done from the start.

Chorus 1

N.C.   A   D
Every little thing she does is magic,

      A   D
Everything she do just turns me on;

      A   D
Even though my life before was tragic

      A
Now I know my love for her goes (on.)

Link 1 | B♭ | Fmaj⁹ | Gadd⁹ | A | Gmaj⁷/B | A/C♯ ‖
on.

Verse 2

       Gadd⁹   **A**

Do I have to tell the story

       Gmaj⁷/B   **A/C♯**   **Gadd⁹** **A** **Gmaj⁷/B** **A/C♯**

Of a thousand rainy days since we first met? _____

      Gadd⁹   **A**

It's a big enough umbrella

      Gmaj⁷/B

But it's always me

     A/C♯   **D**   **G A** │ **D**   **G A** │ **D**   **G A** │ **D**   ‖

That ends up getting wet.

Chorus 2

     N.C.   **A**   **D**

Every little thing she does is magic,

           A   **D**

Everything she do just turns me on;

           A   **D**

Even though my life before was tragic

          A

Now I know my love for her goes (on.)

Link 2

  │ **B♭**   │ **Fmaj⁹** │ **B♭**   │ **Fmaj⁹** │

on.

Bridge

B♭   **Am⁷**   **Gm⁷**   **Am⁷**

  I resolve to call her up   a thousand times a day

Gm⁷   **Am⁷**   **B♭**   **Am⁷**

  And ask her if she'll marry me   in some old-fashioned way.

     B♭   **C**

But my silent fears have gripped me

     B♭   **C**

Long before I reach the phone,

     B♭   **C**

Long before my tongue has tripped me.

     B♭   **C**   **D**   **G A** │ **D**   ‖

Must I always be alone?

Chorus 3

     N.C.   **A**   **D**

Every little thing she does is magic,

           A   **D**

Everything she do just turns me on;

           A   **D**

Even though my life before was tragic

          A   **D**

Now I know my love for her goes on.

Chorus 4

    N.C.   **A**   **D**
Every little thing she does is magic,
                   A   **D**
Everything she do just turns me on;
                 A   **D**
Even though my life before was tragic
                 A
Now I know my love for her goes (on.)

Link 3

| B♭ | Fmaj9 | Gm7 | Am7 | |
on. _____

| B♭ | F C | D | D | ‖

Coda

B♭   **Fmaj9**
  Every little thing, every little thing,
Gm7   **Am7**
Every little thing, every little thing,
B♭   **F**
Every little, every little, every little,
C   **D**
Every little thing she does.
         B♭   **Fmaj9**
Every little thing she does,
         Gm7   **Am7**
Every little thing she does,
         B♭   **F**
Every little thing she does,
      C   **D**
That she does   is magic.
‖: **B♭**   **Fmaj9**   **Gm7**   **Am7**
  Bee-yo-oh, bee-yo-oh, bee-yo-oh,
         B♭   **Fmaj9 C**   **D**
Bee-yo-oh, bee-yo-oh, bee - yo - oh, bee-yo-oh, bee-yo-oh. :‖
B♭   **Fmaj9 Gm7**   **Am7**
  Every little thing,   every little thing,
B♭   **F**   **C**   **D**
  Every little thing she do is magic,

Magic, magic, magic, magic, magic.
B♭   **Fmaj9**   **Gm7 Am7**
Yo - oh,   yo - oh,
     B♭   **C**   **D**
Bee-yo-oh-oh. _____
                  Fade out

King Of Pain

Words & Music by
Sting

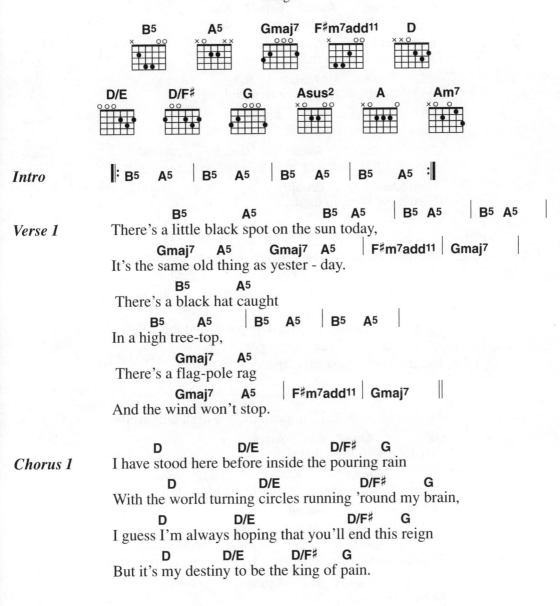

Intro ‖: B5 A5 | B5 A5 | B5 A5 | B5 A5 :‖

Verse 1

          B5   A5   B5 A5 | B5 A5 | B5 A5 |
There's a little black spot on the sun today,

        Gmaj7   A5   Gmaj7   A5 | F♯m7add11 | Gmaj7 |
It's the same old thing as yester - day.

          B5   A5
There's a black hat caught

          B5   A5 | B5 A5 | B5 A5 |
In a high tree-top,

          Gmaj7   A5
There's a flag-pole rag

          Gmaj7   A5 | F♯m7add11 | Gmaj7 ‖
And the wind won't stop.

Chorus 1

         D   D/E   D/F♯   G
I have stood here before inside the pouring rain

         D   D/E   D/F♯   G
With the world turning circles running 'round my brain,

         D   D/E   D/F♯   G
I guess I'm always hoping that you'll end this reign

         D   D/E   D/F♯   G
But it's my destiny to be the king of pain.

Verse 2

    B5   **Asus2** **B5**
There's a little black spot on the sun today,

  B5 **Asus2 B5** **Asus2**
(That's my soul up there)

    Gmaj7 **Asus2** **Gmaj7** **Asus2**
It's the same old thing as yester - day.

 F#m7add11   **Gmaj7**
(That's my soul up there)

     B5 **Asus2** **B5**   **Asus2**
There's a black hat caught in a high tree-top,

 B5 **Asus2 B5** **Asus2**
(That's my soul up there).

    Gmaj7 **Asus2** **Gmaj7** **Asus2**
There's a flag pole rag and the wind won't stop.

 F#m7add11   **Gmaj7**
(That's my soul up there)

Chorus 2

   D   **D/E**   **D/F#** **G**
I have stood here before inside the pouring rain

    D   **D/E**   **D/F#** **G**
With the world turning circles running 'round my brain,

   D   **D/E**   **D/F#** **G**
I guess I'm always hoping that you'll end this reign

   D **D/E** **D/F#** **G**
But it's my destiny to be the king of pain.

Verse 3

    B5   **Asus2 B5**   **Asus2**
There's a fossil that's trapped in a high cliff-wall, ____

 B5 **Asus2 B5** **Asus2**
(That's my soul up there)

   Gmaj7   **Asus2** **Gmaj7 Asus2**
There's a dead salmon frozen in a water - fall .

 F#m7add11   **Gmaj7**
(That's my soul up there)

    B5   **Asus2 B5**   **Asus2**
There's a blue whale beached by a springtide's ebb,

 B5 **Asus2 B5** **Asus2**
(That's my soul up there)

   Gmaj7 **Asus2** **Gmaj7** **Asus2**
There's a butterfly trapped in a spider's web.

 F#m7add11   **Gmaj7**
(That's my soul up there)

Chorus 3   As Chorus 2

Bridge

       A   Gmaj⁷   A   Gmaj⁷   A
There's a king on a throne with his eyes torn out,
         Gmaj⁷   A   Gmaj⁷   A
There's a blind man looking for a shadow of doubt;
        Gmaj⁷   A   Gmaj⁷ A
There's a rich man sleeping on a golden bed,
           Gmaj⁷   A   Gmaj⁷
There's a skeleton   choking on a crust of (bread.)

Solo

| B⁵ Asus² | B⁵ Asus² | B⁵ Asus² | B⁵ Asus² | Gmaj⁷ Asus² |
bread. _____   King of pain.

| Gmaj⁷ Asus² | F♯m⁷add¹¹ | Gmaj⁷ ‖

Link

‖: Am⁷ | Am⁷ | Am⁷ | Am⁷ :‖

Verse 4

           B⁵
There's a red fox torn by a huntsman's pack,
               Asus² B⁵
(That's my soul up   there)
            Asus²
There's a black-winged gull with a broken back.
  F♯m⁷add¹¹   Gmaj⁷
(That's my soul up there)
           N.C.
There's a little black spot on the sun today,
                         F♯m⁷add¹¹ Gmaj⁷
It's the same old thing as yesterday.

Chorus 4

          D   D/E   D/F♯   G
I have stood here before inside the pouring rain
          D   D/E   D/F♯   G
With the world turning circles running 'round my brain,
         D   D/E   D/F♯   G
I guess I'm always hoping that you'll end this reign
         D   D/E   D/F♯   G
But it's my destiny to be the king of pain.

Coda

| D D/E | D/F♯ G ‖: D D/E | D/F♯ G :‖
                   King of   pain,   king of

‖: D   D/E | D/F♯   G :‖
  pain.   I'll   always be king of   *Repeat to fade*

Message In A Bottle

Words & Music by
Sting

C#sus2   Asus2   Bsus2   F#sus2   A   D   E   F#m   C#m

Intro

| C#sus2 Asus2 | Bsus2 F#sus2 | C#sus2 Asus2 | Bsus2 F#sus2 ||

Verse 1

C#sus2 Asus2 Bsus2 F#sus2   C#sus2 Asus2 Bsus2 F#sus2
Just a cast-away, an island lost at sea - o,

C#sus2 Asus2   Bsus2 F#sus2 C#sus2 Asus2   Bsus2 F#sus2
Another lonely day,   no-one here but me - o.

C#sus2 A2sus Bsus2 F#sus2   C#sus2 Asus2   Bsus2 F#sus2
More loneliness than any   man could bear,

C#sus2 Asus2   Bsus2 F#sus2   C#sus2 Asus2 Bsus2 F#sus2
Rescue me before I   fall   into despair - o.

Chorus 1

A   D   E
I'll send an S.O.S. to the world,

A   D   E
I'll send an S.O.S. to the world.

F#m   D
I hope that someone gets my,

F#m   D
I hope that someone gets my,

F#m   D
I hope that someone gets my

C#m   A   C#m | A |
Message in a bottle, yeah,

C#m   A   F#m | F#m ||
Message in a bottle, yeah.

Verse 2

C#sus2 Asus2 Bsus2   F#sus2   C#sus2   Asus2 Bsus2 F#sus2
A year has passed since I wrote my note

C#sus2 Asus2   Bsus2   F#sus2   C#sus2 Asus2 Bsus2 F#sus2
But I should have known this right from the start.

C#sus2 Asus2 Bsus2   F#sus2   C#sus2 Asus2 Bsus2 F#sus2
Only   hope can keep me together,

C#sus2 Asus2   Bsus2   F#sus2 C#sus2 Asus2   Bsus2 F#sus2
Love can mend your life, but love can break your heart.

Chorus 2

```
         A            D    E
      I'll send an S.O.S. to the world,

         A            D    E
      I'll send an S.O.S. to the world.

      F♯m            D
      I hope that someone gets my,

      F♯m            D
      I hope that someone gets my,

      F♯m            D
      I hope that someone gets my

      C♯m          A              C♯m        A
   ‖: Message in a bottle, yeah,            |         :‖  Play 3 times

      C♯m        A           F♯m   F♯m    F♯m    F♯m
      Message in a bottle, yeah. |      |      |      |      ‖
```

Verse 3

```
      C♯sus2 Asus2    Bsus2 F♯sus2 C♯sus2 Asus2    Bsus2 F♯sus2
      Walked out this morning,   I don't  believe what I saw,

      C♯sus2   Asus2  Bsus2 F♯sus2 C♯sus2   Asus2 Bsus2 F♯sus2
      A hundred million bottles   washed up on the shore.

      C♯sus2 Asus2    Bsus2 F♯sus2      C♯sus2 Asus2 Bsus2 F♯sus2
      Seems like I'm not alone in being alone,

      C♯sus2   Asus2  Bsus2  F♯sus2 C♯sus2 Asus2 Bsus2 F♯sus2
      Hundred  million  cast - aways     looking   for  a  home.
```

Chorus 3

```
         A            D    E
      I'll send an S.O.S. to the world,

         A            D    E
      I'll send an S.O.S. to the world.

      F♯m            D
      I hope that someone gets my,

      F♯m            D
      I hope that someone gets my,

      F♯m            D
      I hope that someone gets my

      C♯m          A              C♯m        A
   ‖: Message in a bottle, yeah,            |         :‖  Play 3 times

      C♯m        A           F♯m   F♯m
      Message in a bottle, yeah. |      |
```

Outro

```
      ‖: C♯sus2 Asus2 | Bsus2 F♯sus2 | C♯sus2 Asus2 | Bsus2  F♯sus2 :‖


         C♯sus2 Asus2   Bsus2 F♯sus2
      ‖: I'm sending  out an S.O.S.        :‖  Repeat to fade
```

Roxanne

Words & Music by
Sting

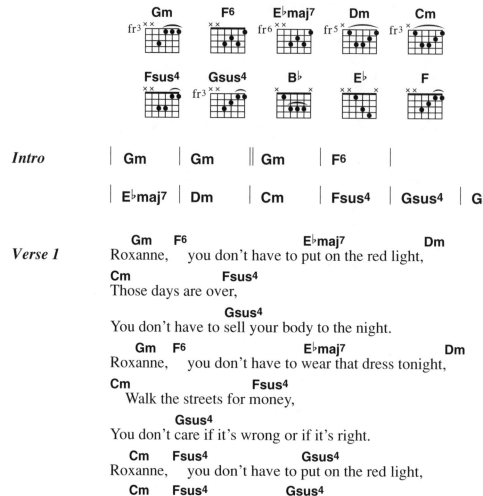

Intro

| Gm | Gm ‖ Gm | F6 |

| E♭maj7 | Dm | Cm | Fsus4 | Gsus4 | Gsus4 ‖

Verse 1

Gm　F6　　　　　　　　E♭maj7　　　　　　Dm
Roxanne,　you don't have to put on the red light,

Cm　　　　　　　　Fsus4
Those days are over,

Gsus4
You don't have to sell your body to the night.

Gm　F6　　　　　　　　E♭maj7　　　　　　　　Dm
Roxanne,　you don't have to wear that dress tonight,

Cm　　　　　　　　Fsus4
　Walk the streets for money,

Gsus4
You don't care if it's wrong or if it's right.

Cm　Fsus4　　　　　Gsus4
Roxanne,　you don't have to put on the red light,

Cm　Fsus4　　　　　Gsus4
Roxanne,　you don't have to put on the red light.

Chorus 1

Cm　B♭
Roxanne, (put on the red light),

E♭　F
Roxanne, (put on the red light),

F　Gm
Roxanne, (put on the red light),

Cm　B♭
Roxanne, (put on the red light),

E♭　F　　　　　　　　　　　Gsus4
Roxanne, (put on the red light), oh.

Instrumental | **Gm** | **Gm** | **Gm** | **Gm** ‖

Verse 2

    Gm   **F6**
I loved you since I knew ya,

    E♭maj7   **Dm**
I wouldn't talk down to ya,

    Cm   **Fsus4**
I have to tell you just how I feel,

      Gsus4
I won't share you with another boy.

Gm   **F6**
I know my mind is made up,

    E♭maj7   **Dm**
So put away your make up,

Cm   **Fsus4**
  Told you once, I won't tell you again,

    Gsus4
It's a crime the way…

     Cm **Fsus4**   **Gsus4**
Roxanne,   you don't have to put on the red light,

     Cm **Fsus4**   **Gsus4**
Roxanne,   you don't have to put on the red light.

Chorus 2

   Cm B♭
‖: Roxanne, (put on the red light),

E♭ **F**
Roxanne, (put on the red light),

F   **Gm**
Roxanne, (put on the red light),

Cm **B♭**
Roxanne, (put on the red light). :‖ *Repeat to fade*

Secret Journey

Words & Music by
Sting

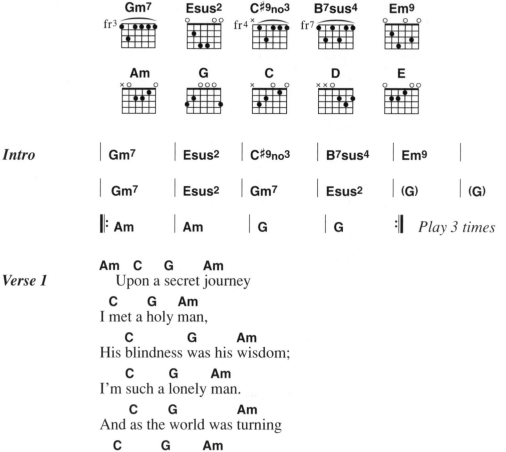

Intro

| Gm7 | Esus2 | C#9no3 | B7sus4 | Em9 | |
| Gm7 | Esus2 | Gm7 | Esus2 | (G) | (G) |
|: Am | Am | G | G :| *Play 3 times*

Verse 1

Am C G Am
   Upon a secret journey

C G Am
I met a holy man,

  C G Am
His blindness was his wisdom;

  C G Am
I'm such a lonely man.

  C G Am
And as the world was turning

C G Am
It rolled itself in pain.

  C G Am
This does not seem to touch you.

  C G Am
He pointed to the rain:

Chorus 1

D E D E
You will see a light in the darkness,

D E D E
You will make some sense of this;

  Am
And when you've made your secret journey

G
You will find this love you miss.

Verse 2

    Am   **C**   **G**   **Am**
And on the days that followed

    C   **G**   **Am**
I listened to his words;

    C   **G**   **Am**
I strained to understand him;

    C   **G**   **Am**
I chased his thoughts like birds.

Chorus 2

D   **E**   **D**   **E**
You will see a light in the darkness,

D   **E**   **D**   **E**
You will make some sense of this;

      Am
And when you've made your secret journey

G
You will find this love you miss.

Instrumental | **Gm⁷** | **Gm⁷** | **C♯⁹ₙₒ³** | **C♯⁹ₙₒ³** ‖

Chorus 3

D   **E**   **D**   **E**
You will see a light in the darkness,

D   **E**   **D**   **E**
You will make some sense of this;

D   **E**   **D**   **E**
You will see joy in this sadness

D   **E**   **D**   **E**
You will find this love you miss.

Coda

      Am
‖: And when you've made your secret journey

G
You will be a holy man.

      Am
And when you've made your secret journey

G
You will be a holy man. :‖ *Repeat to fade*

So Lonely

Words & Music by
Sting

C	G	Am	F	D	A	Bm

Verse 1

C   G   Am   F
Well someone told me yesterday

C   G   Am   F
That when you throw your love away

C   G   Am   F
You act as if you just don't care,

C   G   Am   F
You look as if you're going somewhere.

C   G   Am   F
But I just can't convince myself,

C   G   Am   F
I couldn't live with no-one else,

C   G   Am   F
And I can only play that part

C   G   Am   F
And sit and nurse my broken heart.

Chorus 1

C   G   Am   F
So lonely,   so lonely, so lonely,

C   G   Am   F
So lonely,   so lonely, so lonely,

C   G   Am   F
So lonely,   so lonely, so lonely,

C   G   Am   F
So lonely,   so lonely, so lonely.

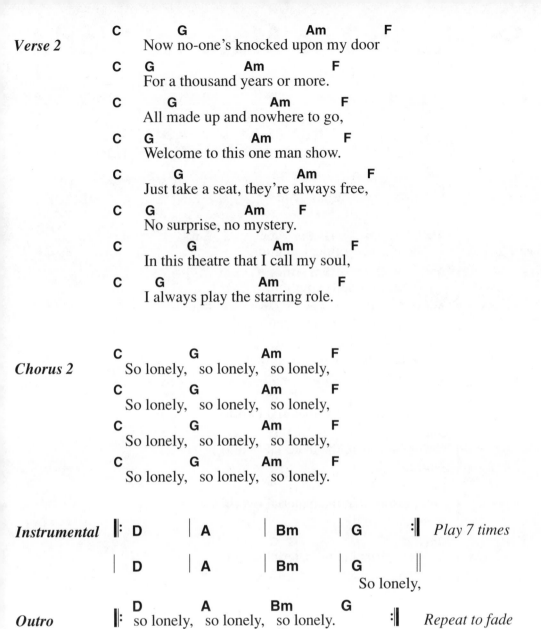

Verse 2

C   G   Am   F
Now no-one's knocked upon my door

C G   Am   F
For a thousand years or more.

C   G   Am   F
All made up and nowhere to go,

C G   Am   F
Welcome to this one man show.

C   G   Am   F
Just take a seat, they're always free,

C G   Am F
No surprise, no mystery.

C   G   Am   F
In this theatre that I call my soul,

C G   Am   F
I always play the starring role.

Chorus 2

C   G   Am   F
So lonely, so lonely, so lonely,

C   G   Am   F
So lonely, so lonely, so lonely,

C   G   Am   F
So lonely, so lonely, so lonely,

C   G   Am   F
So lonely, so lonely, so lonely.

Instrumental ‖: D | A | Bm | G   :‖ *Play 7 times*

| D | A | Bm | G   ‖
So lonely,

Outro ‖: D   A   Bm   G
so lonely, so lonely, so lonely. :‖ *Repeat to fade*

Spirits In The Material World

Words & Music by
Sting

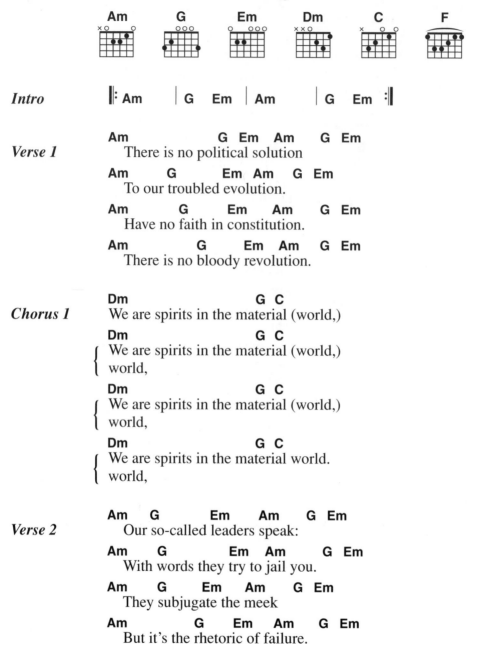

Intro ‖: Am | G Em | Am | G Em :‖

Verse 1

Am   G Em Am   G Em
There is no political solution

Am   G   Em Am G Em
To our troubled evolution.

Am   G   Em   Am   G Em
Have no faith in constitution.

Am   G   Em Am   G Em
There is no bloody revolution.

Chorus 1

Dm   G C
We are spirits in the material (world,)

Dm   G C
{ We are spirits in the material (world,)
{ world,

Dm   G C
{ We are spirits in the material (world,)
{ world,

Dm   G C
{ We are spirits in the material world.
{ world,

Verse 2

Am G   Em   Am   G Em
Our so-called leaders speak:

Am G   Em Am   G Em
With words they try to jail you.

Am G   Em   Am   G Em
They subjugate the meek

Am   G   Em Am   G Em
But it's the rhetoric of failure.

Chorus 2

Dm   **G**   **C**
We are spirits in the material (world,)

{ **Dm**   **G**   **C**
  We are spirits in the material (world,)
  world,

{ **Dm**   **G**   **C**
  We are spirits in the material (world,)
  world,

{ **Dm**   **G**   **C**
  We are spirits in the material
  world,

Dm   **C** | **F**   **G** | **Am**   **G** | **F**   **C Dm** ‖
world. _____

Instrumental ‖: **Am** | **G**   **Em** | **Am** | **G**   **Em** :‖

Verse 3

Am   **G**   **Em**   **Am**   **G Em**
  Where does the answer lie

Am G   **Em**   **Am**   **G Em**
    Living from day to day?

Am   **G**   **Em**   **Am**   **G Em**
  If it's something we can't buy

Am   **G**   **Em Am**   **G Em**
  There must be another way.

Outro

Dm   **G**   **C**
We are spirits in the material (world,)

‖: { **Dm**   **G**   **C**
  We are spirits in the material (world,) :‖ *Repeat to fade*
  world,

Walking On The Moon

Words & Music by
Sting

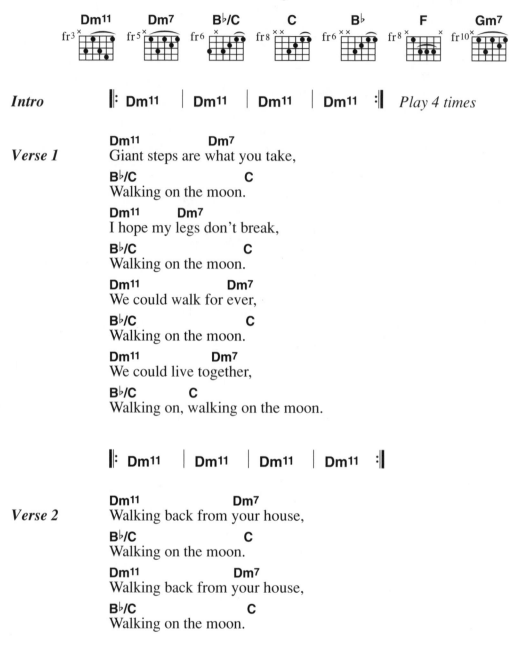

Intro ‖: Dm11 | Dm11 | Dm11 | Dm11 :‖ *Play 4 times*

Verse 1

Dm11   Dm7
Giant steps are what you take,

B♭/C   C
Walking on the moon.

Dm11   Dm7
I hope my legs don't break,

B♭/C   C
Walking on the moon.

Dm11   Dm7
We could walk for ever,

B♭/C   C
Walking on the moon.

Dm11   Dm7
We could live together,

B♭/C   C
Walking on, walking on the moon.

‖: Dm11 | Dm11 | Dm11 | Dm11 :‖

Verse 2

Dm11   Dm7
Walking back from your house,

B♭/C   C
Walking on the moon.

Dm11   Dm7
Walking back from your house,

B♭/C   C
Walking on the moon.

(cont.)

Dm11   Dm7
Feet don't hardly touch the ground,
B♭/C   C
Walking on the moon.

     Dm11   Dm7
My feet don't hardly make no sound,
B♭/C   C | Dm11 | Dm11 ‖
Walking on, walking on the moon.

Bridge 1

B♭   F   C
Some may say,
           Gm7   B♭
I'm wishing my days away.
     F   C
No way,
          Gm7   B♭
And if it's the price I pay
      F   C
Some say,
        Gm7   B♭
Tomorrow's another day.
      F
You'll stay
  C
I may as well play.

Instrumental ‖: Dm11 | Dm11 | Dm11 | Dm11 :‖

Verse 3   As Verse I

Bridge 2   As Bridge 1

           Dm11
Outro   ‖: Keep it up,   keep it up. :‖ *Repeat to fade*

Wrapped Around Your Finger

Words & Music by
Sting

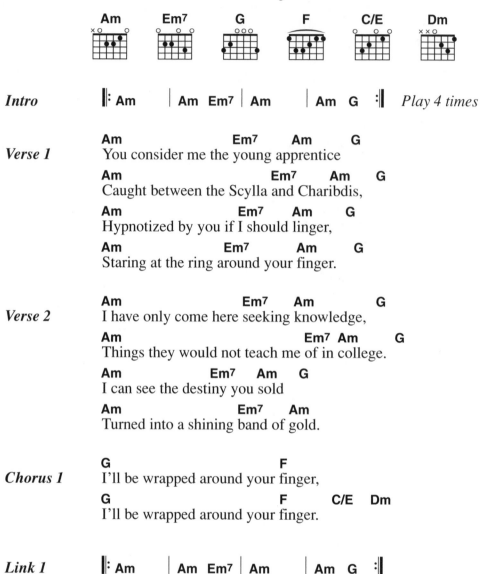

Intro 𝄆 Am │ Am Em7 │ Am │ Am G 𝄇 *Play 4 times*

Verse 1
```
         Am              Em7       Am        G
You consider me the young apprentice
         Am                    Em7       Am   G
Caught between the Scylla and Charibdis,
         Am              Em7       Am        G
Hypnotized by you if I should linger,
         Am              Em7          Am     G
Staring at the ring around your finger.
```

Verse 2
```
         Am                 Em7      Am           G
I have only come here seeking knowledge,
         Am                          Em7 Am       G
Things they would not teach me of in college.
         Am          Em7    Am    G
I can see the destiny you sold
         Am                 Em7     Am
Turned into a shining band of gold.
```

Chorus 1
```
G                          F
I'll be wrapped around your finger,
G                          F      C/E   Dm
I'll be wrapped around your finger.
```

Link 1 𝄆 Am │ Am Em7 │ Am │ Am G 𝄇

Verse 3

```
Am                   Em7    Am    G
Mephistopheles is not your   name
        Am                     Em7   Am   G
But I know what you're up to just the same.
Am              Em7    Am    G
I will listen hard to your tuition
Am                     Em7    Am
You will see it come to its fruition.
```

Chorus 2

```
G                              F
I'll be wrapped around your finger,
G                          F       C/E   Dm
I'll be wrapped around your finger.
```

Link 2

‖: Am | Am   Em7 | Am | Am   G   :‖

Verse 4

```
Am          Em7              F         G
Devil and the deep blue sea behind me,
Dm          Em7              F         G
Vanish in the air you'll never find me.
Am          Em7        F          G
I will turn your face to alabaster _____
Dm                  Em7              F
When you find your servant is your master.
```

Chorus 3

```
        G                          F
Oh, you'll be wrapped around my finger,
G                          F
You'll be wrapped around my finger,
G                          F       C/E   Dm
You'll be wrapped around my finger.
```

Coda

‖: Am | Am   Em7 | Am | Am   G   :‖ *Repeat to fade*

Synchronicity II

Words & Music by
Sting

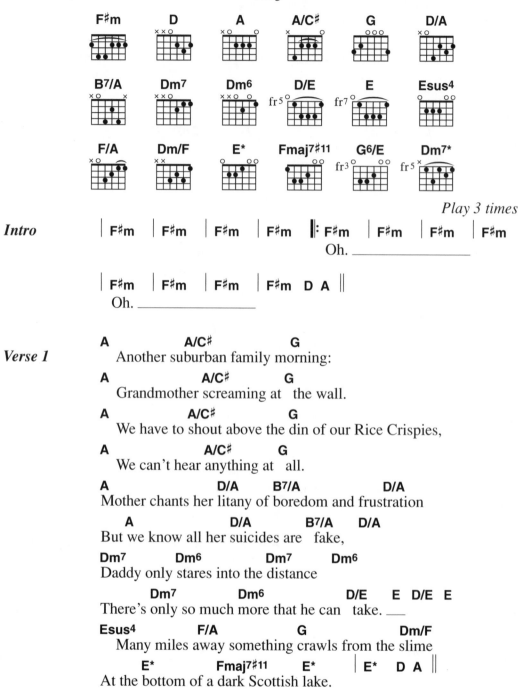

Play 3 times

Intro | F#m | F#m | F#m | F#m ‖: F#m | F#m | F#m | F#m :‖

Oh. _____

| F#m | F#m | F#m | F#m D A ‖

Oh. _____

Verse 1

A   A/C#   G
Another suburban family morning:

A   A/C#   G
Grandmother screaming at   the wall.

A   A/C#   G
We have to shout above the din of our Rice Crispies,

A   A/C#   G
We can't hear anything at   all.

A   D/A   B7/A   D/A
Mother chants her litany of boredom and frustration

A   D/A   B7/A D/A
But we know all her suicides are   fake,

Dm7   Dm6   Dm7   Dm6
Daddy only stares into the distance

Dm7   Dm6   D/E   E D/E E
There's only so much more that he can   take. ___

Esus4   F/A   G   Dm/F
Many miles away something crawls from the slime

E*   Fmaj7#11   E* | E* D A ‖
At the bottom of a dark Scottish lake.

Verse 2

```
         A              A/C♯              G
       Another industrial ugly morning:
          A                A/C♯        G
       The factory belches filth into the  sky.
       A              A/C♯                   G
          He walks unhindered through the picket lines today,
       A                A/C♯            G
          He doesn't think to wonder   why.
           A            D/A
       The secretaries pout and preen
            B7/A               D/A
       Like cheap tarts in a red-light street,
            A            D/A            B7/A    D/A
       But all he ever thinks to do is watch,
           Dm7           Dm6             Dm7                    Dm6
       And every single meeting with his so-called superior
           Dm7                  Dm6
       Is a humiliating kick in the crotch.
```

```
      | D/E   E  | D/E   E  |
      Esus4          F/A            G
      Many miles away something crawls
           Dm/F         E                    Fmaj7♯11  E*
      To the surface of a dark Scottish loch.
```

Instrumental

```
      ‖: (F♯m)  | (F♯m)  | (F♯m)  | (F♯m)  :‖   Play 3 times

      | (F♯m)  | (F♯m)  | (F♯m)  | (F♯m)  D A ‖
```

Verse 3

```
         A             A/C♯                  G
       Another working day has ended:
       A             A/C♯          G
          Only the rush-hour hell   to face
       A                  A/C♯              G
          Packed like lemmings into shiny metal boxes,
           A           A/C♯      G
       Contestants in a suicidal   race.
       A                 D/A
       Daddy grips the wheel
               B7/A           D/A
       And stares alone into the distance
           A                     D/A                 B7/A     D/A
       He knows that something somewhere has to break.
```

cont.

Dm7   Dm6   Dm7   Dm6

He sees the family home now looming in his headlights,

Dm7

The pain upstairs

Dm6   D/E   E* | D/E   E* |

That makes his eyeballs   ache. _____

| D/E   E* | D/E   E* |

Esus4   F/A   G   Dm/F

Many miles away there's a shadow on the door

E*   Fmaj7#11   G6 Dm7*

Of a cottage on the shore of a   dark   Scottish (lake.)

Coda

| E* | Fmaj7#11 | G6/E | Dm7* |

lake. _____

| E* | Fmaj7#11 | G6/E | Dm7* |

                                              Many miles a -

‖: E* | Fmaj7#11 | G6/E | Dm7*   :‖ *Repeat to fade*

- way.   Many miles a -